50 Easy to play Children's Favourite Hymns & Songs

kevin mayhew

Important Copyright Information

We would like to remind users of this hymnal that the reproduction of any song texts or music without the permission of the copyright holder is illegal. Details of all copyright holders are clearly indicated under each song.

Many of the song *texts* may be covered either by a Christian Copyright Licensing (CCL) licence or a Calamus licence. If you possess a CCL or Calamus licence, it is essential that you check your instruction manual to ensure that the song you wish to use is covered.

If you are *not* a member of CCL or Calamus, or the song you wish to reproduce is not covered by your licence, you must contact the copyright holder direct for their permission.

Christian Copyright Licensing (Europe) Ltd, have also now introduced a *Music Reproduction Licence*. Again, if you hold such a licence it is essential that you check your instruction manual to ensure that the song you wish to reproduce is covered. The reproduction of any music not covered by your licence is both illegal and immoral.

If you are interested in joining CCL or Calamus, they can be contacted at the following addresses:

Christian Copyright Licensing (Europe) Ltd,
PO Box 1339, Eastbourne, East Sussex BN21 1AD.
Tel: 01323 417711 Fax: 01323 417722

Calamus,
30 North Terrace, Mildenhall, Suffolk, IP28 7AB.
Tel: 01638 716579 Fax: 01638 510390

First published in Great Britain in 2001 by Kevin Mayhew Ltd
Buxhall, Stowmarket, Suffolk IP14 3BW
Tel: +44 (0) 1449 737978 Fax: +44 (0) 1449 737834
E-mail: info@kevinmayhewltd.com

www.kevinmayhew.com

© Copyright 2001 Kevin Mayhew Ltd.

9 8 7 6 5

ISBN 978 1 84003 812 5
ISMN M 57004 935 6
Catalogue No. 1400297

Cover design: Melody-Anne Lee
Music setting: Donald Thomson
Proof reading: Geoffrey Moore

Printed and bound in Great Britain

Index of First lines
Song titles are shown indented and in italics

1 Abba, Father, let me be

Words and Music: Dave Bilbrough
arr. Christopher Tambling

Ab-ba, Fa-ther, let me be yours and yours a-lone. May my will for e-ver be more and more your own. Ne-ver let my heart grow cold, ne-ver let me go. Ab-ba, Fa-ther, let me be yours and yours a-lone.

2 Alleluia, alleluia, give thanks to the risen Lord

Words and Music: Donald Fishel
arr. Alan Ridout

2. Spread the good news o'er all the earth,
Jesus has died and has risen.

3. Come, let us praise the living God,
joyfully sing to our Saviour.

3 All over the world

Words and Music: Roy Turner
arr. Noel Rawsthorne

1. All ov-er the world the Spi-rit is mov-ing, all o-ver the world, as the pro-phets said it would be. All o-ver the world there's a migh-ty re-ve-la-tion of the glo-ry of the Lord, as the wa-ters co-ver the sea.

2. All over this land the Spirit is moving,
   all over this land,
   as the prophets said it would be.
   All over this land
   there's a mighty revelation
   of the glory of the Lord,
   as the waters cover the sea.

3. All over the Church the Spirit is moving,
   all over the Church,
   as the prophets said it would be.
   All over the Church
   there's a mighty revelation
   of the glory of the Lord,
   as the waters cover the sea.

4. All over us all the Spirit is moving,
   all over us all,
   as the prophets said it would be.
   All over us all
   there's a mighty revelation
   of the glory of the Lord,
   as the waters cover the sea.

5. Deep down in my heart, the Spirit is moving,
   deep down in my heart,
   as the prophets said it would be.
   Deep down in my heart,
   there's a mighty revelation
   of the glory of the Lord,
   as the waters cover the sea.

4 All things bright and beautiful

Words: Cecil Frances Alexander
Music: traditional English melody arr. Alan Ridout

TUNE 1: ALL THINGS BRIGHT AND BEAUTIFUL

See overleaf for alternative tune

2. The purple-headed mountain,
   the river running by,
   the sunset and the morning
   that brightens up the sky.

3. The cold wind in the winter,
   the pleasant summer sun, ·
   the ripe fruits in the garden,
   he made them ev'ry one.

4. He gave us eyes to see them,
   and lips that we might tell
   how great is God Almighty
   who has made all things well.

Words: Cecil Frances Alexander
Music: traditional English melody arr. Alan Ridout

TUNE 2: ROYAL OAK

2. The purple-headed mountain,
   the river running by,
   the sunset and the morning
   that brightens up the sky.

3. The cold wind in the winter,
   the pleasant summer sun,
   the ripe fruits in the garden,
   he made them ev'ry one.

4. He gave us eyes to see them,
   and lips that we might tell
   how great is God Almighty
   who has made all things well.

5 Be still, for the presence of the Lord

Words and Music: David J. Evans
arr. Christopher Tambling

2. Be still, for the glory of the Lord is shining all around;
   he burns with holy fire, with splendour he is crowned.
   How awesome is the sight, our radiant King of light!
   Be still, for the glory of the Lord is shining all around.

3. Be still, for the power of the Lord is moving in this place;
   he comes to cleanse and heal, to minister his grace.
   No work too hard for him, in faith receive from him.
   Be still, for the power of the Lord is moving in this place.

6 Bind us together, Lord

Words and Music: Bob Gillman
arr. Alan Ridout

Steadily, not too fast

Refrain

2. Fit for the glory of God,
purchased by his precious Blood,
born with the right to be free;
Jesus the vict'ry has won.

3. We are the fam'ly of God,
we are his promise divine,
we are his chosen desire,
we are the glorious new wine.

7 Colours of day

Light up the fire

Words and Music: Sue McClellan, John Paculabo and Keith Ryecroft
arr. Alan Ridout

2. Go through the park, on into the town;
   the sun still shines on, it never goes down.
   The light of the world is risen again;
   the people of darkness are needing a friend.

3. Open your eyes, look into the sky,
   the darkness has come, the sun came to die.
   The evening draws on, the sun disappears,
   but Jesus is living, his Spirit is near.

8 Come on and celebrate!

Celebrate

Words and Music: Patricia Morgan
arr. Christopher Tambling

9 Don't build your house on the sandy land

Sandy land

Words and Music: Karen Lafferty
arr. Noel Rawsthorne

This may be sung as a round with entries indicated by A *and* B

10 Father, I place into your hands

Words and Music: Jenny Hewer
arr. Christopher Tambling

2. Father, I place into your hands
   my friends and family.
   Father, I place into your hands
   the things that trouble me.
   Father, I place into your hands
   the person I would be,
   for I know I always can trust you.

3. Father, we love to seek your face,
   we love to hear your voice.
   Father, we love to sing your praise
   and in your name rejoice.
   Father, we love to walk with you
   and in your presence rest,
   for we know we always can trust you.

4. Father, I want to be with you
   and do the things you do.
   Father, I want to speak the words
   that you are speaking too.
   Father, I want to love the ones
   that you will draw to you,
   for I know that I am one with you.

11 Father, we adore you

Words and Music: Terrye Coelho
arr. Christopher Tambling

This may be sung as a round with entries indicated by A *,* B *and* C

2. Jesus, we adore you,
lay our lives before you,
How we love you!

3. Spirit, we adore you,
lay our lives before you,
How we love you!

12 From heaven you came

The Servant King

Words and Music: Graham Kendrick
arr. Christopher Tambling

2. There in the garden of tears,
   my heavy load he chose to bear;
   his heart with sorrow was torn,
   'Yet not my will, but yours,' he said.

3. Come, see his hands and his feet,
   the scars that speak of sacrifice,
   hands that flung stars into space
   to cruel nails surrendered.

4. So let us learn how to serve,
   and in our lives enthrone him;
   each other's needs to prefer,
   for it is Christ we're serving.

13 Give me joy in my heart

Sing hosanna

Words and Music: traditional
arr. John Ballantine

2. Give me peace in my heart, keep me resting,
   give me peace in my heart, I pray.
   Give me peace in my heart, keep me resting,
   keep me resting till the end of day.

3. Give me love in my heart, keep me serving,
   give me love in my heart, I pray.
   Give me love in my heart, keep me serving,
   keep me serving till the end of day.

4. Give me oil in my lamp, keep me burning,
   give me oil in my lamp, I pray.
   Give me oil in my lamp, keep me burning,
   keep me burning till the end of day.

14 God forgave my sin

Freely, freely

Words and Music: Carol Owens
arr. Christopher Tambling

2. All pow'r is giv'n in Jesus' name,
   in earth and heav'n in Jesus' name;
   and in Jesus' name I come to you
   to share his pow'r as he told me to.

3. God gives us life in Jesus' name,
   he lives in us in Jesus' name;
   and in Jesus' name I come to you
   to share his peace as he told me to.

15 Halle, halle, halle

Words: traditional
Music: unknown arr. Noel Rawsthorne

Hal - le, hal - le, hal - le - lu - jah! Hal - le, hal - le, hal -

- le - lu - jah! Hal - le, hal - le, hal - le -

lu - jah! Hal - le - lu - jah, hal - le - lu - jah!

16 Have you heard the raindrops

Water of life

Words and Music: Christian Strover
arr. Noel Rawsthorne

1. Have you heard the rain-drops drum-ming on the roof-tops? Have you heard the rain-drops drip-ping on the ground? Have you heard the rain-drops splash-ing in the streams and run-ning to the ri-vers all a-round? There's wa-ter, wa-ter of life, Je-sus gives us the wa-ter of life; there's wa-ter, wa-ter of life, Je-sus gives us the wa-ter of life.

2. There's a busy worker digging in the desert,
   digging with a spade that flashes in the sun;
   soon there will be water rising in the well-shaft,
   spilling from the bucket as it comes.

3. Nobody can live who hasn't any water,
   when the land is dry, then nothing much grows;
   Jesus gives us life if we drink the living water,
   sing it so that ev'rybody knows.

17 He's got the whole world in his hand

Words and Music: traditional
arr. Alan Ridout

2. He's got you and me, brother, in his hand. *(x3)*
   He's got the whole world in his hand.

3. He's got you and me, sister, in his hand. *(x3)*
   He's got the whole world in his hand.

4. He's got the little tiny baby in his hand. *(x3)*
   He's got the whole world in his hand.

5. He's got ev'rybody here in his hand. *(x3)*
   He's got the whole world in his hand.

18 I danced in the morning

Lord of the Dance

Words: Sydney Carter
Music: Shaker melody adapted by Sydney Carter
arr. Noel Rawsthorne

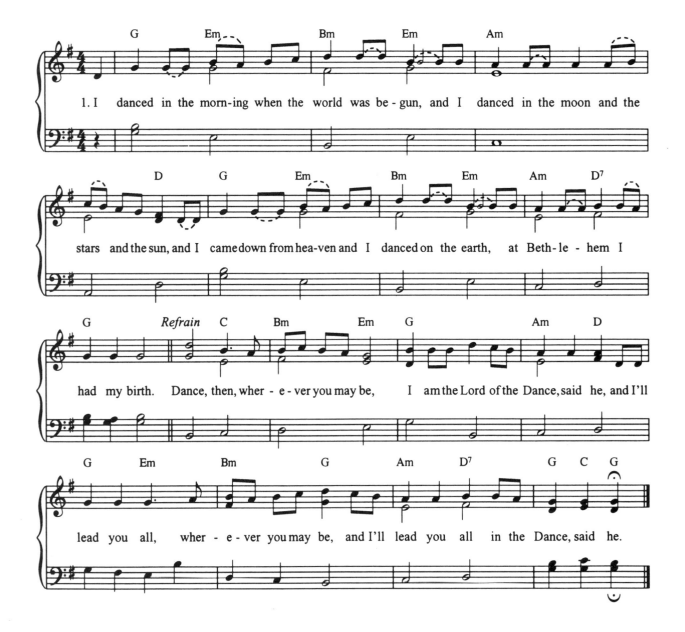

1. I danced in the morn-ing when the world was be-gun, and I danced in the moon and the stars and the sun, and I came down from hea-ven and I danced on the earth, at Beth-le-hem I had my birth. Dance, then, wher-e-ver you may be, I am the Lord of the Dance, said he, and I'll lead you all, wher-e-ver you may be, and I'll lead you all in the Dance, said he.

2. I danced for the scribe and the pharisee,
   but they would not dance and they wouldn't follow me,
   I danced for the fishermen, for James and John –
   they came with me and the Dance went on.

3. I danced on the Sabbath and I cured the lame;
   the holy people said it was a shame.
   They whipped and they stripped and they hung me on high,
   and they left me there on a Cross to die.

4. I danced on a Friday when the sky turned black –
   it's hard to dance with the devil on your back.
   They buried my body, and they thought I'd gone,
   but I am the Dance, and I still go on.

5. They cut me down and I leapt up high;
   I am the life that'll never, never die;
   I'll live in you if you'll live in me –
   I am the Lord of the Dance, said he.

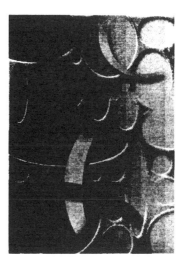

19 If I were a butterfly

The butterfly song

Words and Music: Brian Howard
arr. Noel Rawsthorne

Refrain

For you gave me a heart, and you gave me a smile, you

gave me Je-sus and you made me your child, and I just thank you,

Fa-ther, for mak-ing me 'me'.

2. If I were an elephant,
   I'd thank you, Lord, by raising my trunk,
   and if I were a kangaroo,
   you know I'd walk right up to you,
   and if I were an octopus,
   I'd thank you, Lord, for my fine looks,
   but I just thank you, Father, for making me 'me'.

3. If I were a wiggly worm,
   I'd thank you, Lord, that I could squirm,
   and if I were a billy goat,
   I'd thank you, Lord, for my strong throat,
   and if I were a fuzzy wuzzy bear,
   I'd thank you, Lord, for my fuzzy wuzzy hair,
   but I just thank you, Father, for making me 'me'.

20 I, the Lord of sea and sky

Here I am, Lord

Words: Dan Schutte, based on Isaiah 6
Music: Dan Schutte arr. Noel Rawsthorne

2. I, the Lord of snow and rain,
   I have borne my people's pain.
   I have wept for love of them.
   They turn away.
   I will break their hearts of stone,
   give them hearts for love alone.
   I will speak my word to them.
   Whom shall I send?

3. I, the Lord of wind and flame,
   I will tend the poor and lame.
   I will set a feast for them.
   My hand will save.
   Finest bread I will provide,
   till their hearts be satisfied.
   I will give my life to them.
   Whom shall I send?

21 It's me, O Lord

Standing in the need of prayer

Words and Music: Spiritual
arr. Noel Rawsthorne

It's me, it's me, it's me, O Lord, standing in the need of prayer. It's
me, it's me, it's me, O Lord, standing in the need of prayer.

1. Not my bro-ther or my sis-ter, but it's me, O Lord, standing in the need of prayer. Not my
bro-ther or my sis-ter, but it's me, O Lord, standing in the need of prayer. It's

2. Not my mother or my father,
   but it's me, O Lord,
   standing in the need of prayer.
   Not my mother or my father,
   but it's me, O Lord,
   standing in the need of prayer.

3. Not the stranger or my neighbour,
   but it's me, O Lord,
   standing in the need of prayer.
   Not the stranger or my neighbour,
   but it's me, O Lord,
   standing in the need of prayer.

22 Jesus' love is very wonderful

Words: H.W. Rattle
Music: unknown arr. Noel Rawsthorne

23 Jubilate, everybody

Words and Music: Fred Dunn
arr. Christopher Tambling

24 Kum ba yah

Words and Music: Spiritual
arr. Alan Ridout

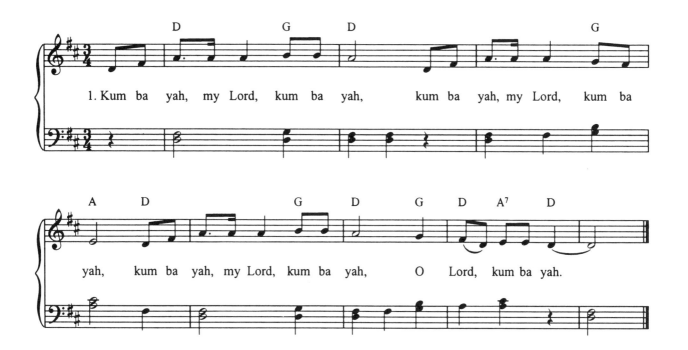

2. Someone's crying, Lord, kum ba yah,
   someone's crying, Lord, kum ba yah,
   someone's crying, Lord, kum ba yah,
   O Lord, kum ba yah.

3. Someone's singing, Lord, kum ba yah,
   someone's singing, Lord, kum ba yah,
   someone's singing, Lord, kum ba yah,
   O Lord, kum ba yah.

4. Someone's praying, Lord, kum ba yah,
   someone's praying, Lord, kum ba yah,
   someone's praying, Lord, kum ba yah,
   O Lord, kum ba yah.

25 Lord Jesus Christ

Living Lord

Words and Music: Patrick Appleford
arr. Noel Rawsthorne

Verse 2 is suitable for Communion.

2. Lord Jesus Christ,
   now and ev'ry day
   teach us how to pray,
   Son of God.
   You have commanded us to do
   this in remembrance, Lord, of you,
   into our lives your pow'r breaks through,
   living Lord.

3. Lord Jesus Christ,
   you have come to us,
   born as one of us,
   Mary's Son.
   Led out to die on Calvary,
   risen from death to set us free,
   living Lord Jesus, help us see
   you are Lord.

4. Lord Jesus Christ,
   I would come to you,
   live my life for you,
   Son of God.
   All your commands I know are true,
   your many gifts will make me new,
   into my life your pow'r breaks through,
   living Lord.

26 Lord of all hopefulness

Words: Jan Struther
Music: traditional Irish melody arr. Alan Ridout

1. Lord of all hope-ful-ness, Lord of all joy, whose trust, e-ver child-like, no cares could des-troy, be there at our wak-ing and give us, we pray, your bliss in our hearts, Lord, at the break of the day.

2. Lord of all eagerness,
   Lord of all faith,
   whose strong hands were skilled
   at the plane and the lathe,
   be there at our labours
   and give us, we pray,
   your strength in our hearts, Lord,
   at the noon of the day.

3. Lord of all kindliness,
   Lord of all grace,
   your hands swift to welcome,
   your arms to embrace,
   be there at our homing
   and give us, we pray,
   your love in our hearts, Lord,
   at the eve of the day.

4. Lord of all gentleness,
   Lord of all calm,
   whose voice is contentment,
   whose presence is balm,
   be there at our sleeping
   and give us, we pray,
   your peace in our hearts, Lord,
   at the end of the day.

27 Lord, the light of your love

Shine, Jesus, shine

Words and Music: Graham Kendrick
arr. Christopher Tambling

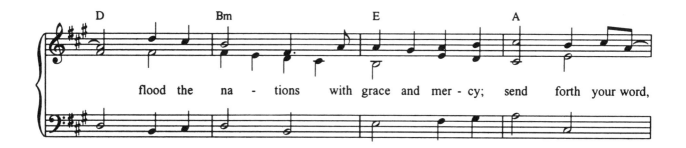

flood the na - tions with grace and mer - cy; send forth your word,

Lord, and let there be light!

2. Lord, I come to your awesome presence,
   from the shadows into your radiance;
   by the blood I may enter your brightness,
   search me, try me, consume all my darkness.
   Shine on me, shine on me.

3. As we gaze on your kingly brightness,
   so our faces display your likeness,
   ever changing from glory to glory,
   mirrored here, may our lives tell your story.
   Shine on me, shine on me.

28 Make me a channel of your peace

The Prayer of St Francis

Words: Sebastian Temple based on the Prayer of St Frances of Assisi
Music: Sebastian Temple arr. Alan Ridout

loved, as to love with all my soul.   4. Make me a chan-nel of your

peace.   It is in par - don - ing that we are par-doned,   in

giv-ing of our-selves that we re - ceive,   and in dy-ing that we're born to e-ter-nal life.

29 Morning has broken

Words: Eleanor Farjeon
Music: traditional Irish melody arr. Alan Ridout

1. Morn-ing has bro - ken like the first morn - ing, black-bird has spo - ken like the first bird. Praise for the sing - ing! Praise for the morn - ing! Praise for them, spring - ing fresh from the Word!

2. Sweet the rain's new fall,
   sunlit from heaven,
   like the first dew-fall
   on the first grass.
   Praise for the sweetness
   of the wet garden,
   sprung in completeness
   where his feet pass.

3. Mine is the sunlight!
   Mine is the morning,
   born of the one light
   Eden saw play.
   Praise with elation,
   praise ev'ry morning,
   God's re-creation
   of the new day!

30 O Lord, all the world belongs to you

Words and Music: Patrick Appleford
arr. Noel Rawsthorne

1. O Lord, all the world be-longs to you, and you are al-ways mak-ing all things new. What is wrong you for-give, and the new life you give is what's turn-ing the world up - side down.

2. The world's only loving to its friends,
   but you have brought us love that never ends;
   loving enemies too,
   and this loving with you
   is what's turning the world upside down.

3. This world lives divided and apart.
   You draw us all together and we start,
   in your body, to see
   that in fellowship we
   can be turning the world upside down.

4. The world wants the wealth to live in state,
   but you show us a new way to be great:
   like a servant you came,
   and if we do the same,
   we'll be turning the world upside down.

5. O Lord, all the world belongs to you,
   and you are always making all things new.
   Send your Spirit on all
   in your Church, whom you call
   to be turning the world upside down.

31 One more step along the world I go

Words and Music: Sydney Carter
arr. Noel Rawsthorne

1. One more step a-long the world I go, one more step a-long the world I go.
From the old things to the new keep me tra-vel-ling a-long with you. And it's
from the old I tra-vel to the new, keep me tra-vel-ling a-long with you.

2. Round the corners of the world I turn,
   more and more about the world I learn.
   All the new things that I see
   you'll be looking at along with me.

3. As I travel through the bad and good,
   keep me travelling the way I should.
   Where I see no way to go
   you'll be telling me the way, I know.

4. Give me courage when the world is rough,
   keep me loving though the world is tough.
   Leap and sing in all I do,
   keep me travelling along with you.

5. You are older than the world can be,
   you are younger than the life in me.
   Ever old and ever new,
   keep me travelling along with you.

32 Our God is so great

Words and Music: unknown
arr. John Ballantine

Our God is so great, so strong and so migh-ty, there's no-thing that he can-not do. Our ri-vers are his, the moun-tains are his, the stars are his han-di-work too.

33 O when the saints go marching in

Words and Music: traditional
arr. Noel Rawsthorne

2. O when they crown him Lord of all,
   O when they crown him Lord of all,
   I want to be in that number
   when they crown him Lord of all.

3. O when all knees bow at his name,
   O when all knees bow at his name,
   I want to be in that number
   when all knees bow at his name.

4. O when they sing the Saviour's praise,
   O when they sing the Saviour's praise,
   I want to be in that number
   when they sing the Saviour's praise.

5. O when the saints go marching in,
   O when the saints go marching in,
   I want to be in that number
   when the saints go marching in.

34 Peace, perfect peace, is the gift

Words and Music: Kevin Mayhew

2. Love, perfect love,
   is the gift of Christ our Lord.
   Love, perfect love,
   is the gift of Christ our Lord.
   Thus, says the Lord,
   will the world know my friends.
   Love, perfect love,
   is the gift of Christ our Lord.

3. Faith, perfect faith,
   is the gift of Christ our Lord.
   Faith, perfect faith,
   is the gift of Christ our Lord.
   Thus, says the Lord,
   will the world know my friends.
   Faith, perfect faith,
   is the gift of Christ our Lord.

4. Hope, perfect hope,
   is the gift of Christ our Lord.
   Hope, perfect hope,
   is the gift of Christ our Lord.
   Thus, says the Lord,
   will the world know my friends.
   Hope, perfect hope,
   is the gift of Christ our Lord.

5. Joy, perfect joy,
   is the gift of Christ our Lord.
   Joy, perfect joy,
   is the gift of Christ our Lord.
   Thus, says the Lord,
   will the world know my friends.
   Joy, perfect joy,
   is the gift of Christ our Lord.

35 Rejoice in the Lord always

Words: Evelyn Tarner based on Philippians 4:4
Music: Evelyn Tarner arr. Christopher Tambling

This may be sung as a round with entries indicated by A *and* B

36 Seek ye first the kingdom of God

Words: v.1 Karen Lafferty; v.2&3 unknown, based on Matthew 6:33; 7:7
Music: Karen Lafferty arr. Christopher Tambling

This may be sung as a round with the second voices entering at the refrain.

2. You shall not live by bread alone,
   but by ev'ry word
   that proceeds from the mouth of God;
   allelu, alleluia.

3. Ask and it shall be given unto you,
   seek and ye shall find;
   knock and it shall be opened unto you;
   allelu, alleluia.

37 Thank you for the summer morning

Words and Music: Susan Sayers
arr. Noel Rawsthorne

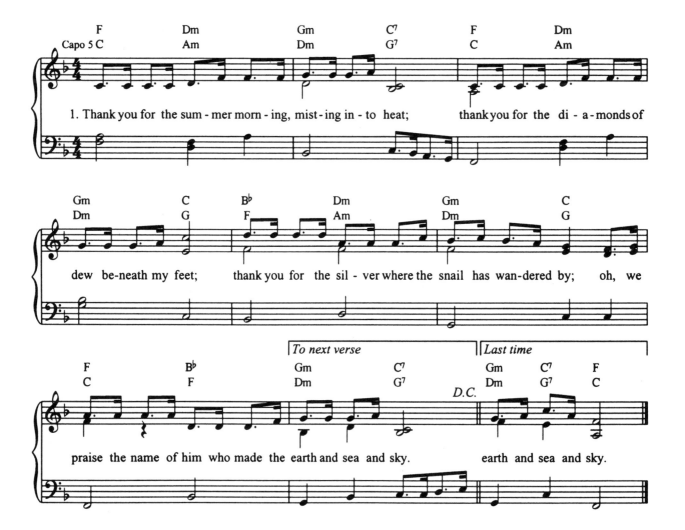

2. Thank you for the yellow fields
of corn like waving hair;
thank you for the red surprise
of poppies here and there;
thank you for the blue of
an electric dragonfly;
oh, we praise the name
of him who made
the earth and sea and sky.

3. Thank you for the splintered light
among the brooding trees;
thank you for the leaves that rustle
in a sudden breeze;
thank you for the branches
and the fun of climbing high;
oh, we praise the name
of him who made
the earth and sea and sky.

4. Thank you for the ev'ning
as the light begins to fade;
clouds so red and purple
that the setting sun has made;
thank you for the shadows
as the owls come gliding by;
oh, we praise the name
of him who made
the earth and sea and sky.

38 Thank you, Lord

Right where we are

Words: Diane Davis Andrew adapted by Geoffrey Marshall-Taylor
Music: Diane Davis Andrew arr. Noel Rawsthorne

Thank you, Lord, for this new day, thank you, Lord, for this new day, thank you, Lord, for this new day, right where we are.

Alleluia, praise the Lord, alleluia, praise the Lord, alleluia, praise the Lord, right where we are.

2. Thank you, Lord, for food to eat,
   thank you, Lord, for food to eat,
   thank you, Lord, for food to eat,
   right where we are.

3. Thank you, Lord, for clothes to wear,
   thank you, Lord, for clothes to wear,
   thank you, Lord, for clothes to wear,
   right where we are.

4. Thank you, Lord, for all your gifts,
   thank you, Lord, for all your gifts,
   thank you, Lord, for all your gifts,
   right where we are.

39 There are hundreds of sparrows

God knows me

Words: John Gowans
Music: John Larsson arr. Noel Rawsthorne

2. There are hundreds of flowers, thousands, millions,
   and flowers fair the meadows wear for all to see;
   there are hundreds and thousands, millions of flowers,
   but God knows ev'ry one, and God knows me.

3. There are hundreds of planets, thousands, millions,
   way out in space each has a place by God's decree;
   there are hundreds and thousands, millions of planets,
   but God knows ev'ry one, and God knows me.

4. There are hundreds of children, thousands, millions,
   and yet their names are written on God's memory;
   there are hundreds and thousands, millions of children,
   but God knows ev'ry one, and God knows me.

40 There is a green hill

Words: Cecil Frances Alexander alt.
Music: William Horsley arr. Noel Rawsthorne

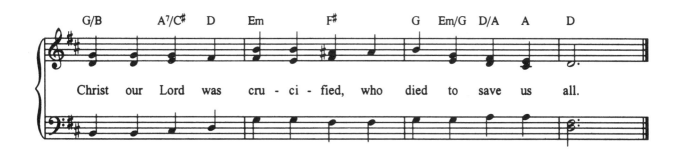

2. We may not know, we cannot tell,
   what pains he had to bear,
   but we believe it was for us
   he hung and suffered there.

3. He died that we could be forgiv'n,
   that God might call us good,
   that we might go at last to heav'n,
   saved by his precious blood.

4. O dearly, dearly has he loved,
   so let us love him too,
   and trust in his redeeming blood,
   and try his works to do.

41 The Spirit lives to set us free

Walk in the light

Words: Damian Lundy
Music: unknown arr. Noel Rawsthorne

1. The Spi-rit lives to set us free, walk, walk in the light. He binds us all in

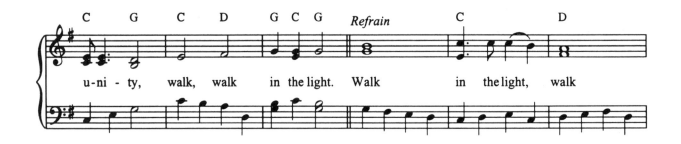

u-ni-ty, walk, walk in the light. *Refrain* Walk in the light, walk

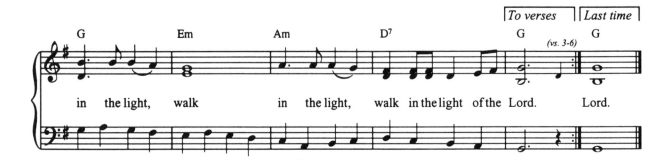

in the light, walk in the light, walk in the light of the Lord. Lord.

2. Jesus promised life to all,
   walk, walk in the light.
   The dead were wakened by his call,
   walk, walk in the light.

3. He died in pain on Calvary,
   walk, walk in the light,
   to save the lost like you and me,
   walk, walk in the light.

4. We know his death was not the end,
   walk, walk in the light.
   He gave his Spirit to be our friend,
   walk, walk in the light.

5. By Jesus' love our wounds are healed,
   walk, walk in the light.
   The Father's kindness is revealed,
   walk, walk in the light.

6. The Spirit lives in you and me,
   walk, walk in the light.
   His light will shine for all to see,
   walk, walk in the light.

42 Think of a world without any flowers

Words: Doreen Newport
Music: Graham Westcott arr. Noel Rawsthorne

2. Think of a world without any animals,
   think of a field without any herd,
   think of a stream without any fishes,
   think of a dawn without any bird.
   We thank you, Lord, for all your living creatures,
   we thank you, Lord, and praise your holy name.

3. Think of a world without any people,
   think of a street with no one living there,
   think of a town without any houses,
   no one to love and nobody to care.
   We thank you, Lord, for families and friendships,
   we thank you, Lord, and praise your holy name.

43 This is the day

Words and Music: Les Garrett
arr. Noel Rawsthorne

2. This is the day, this is the day
   when he rose again, when he rose again;
   we will rejoice, we will rejoice,
   and be glad in it, and be glad in it.
   This is the day when he rose again;
   we will rejoice and be glad in it.
   This is the day, this is the day
   when he rose again.

3. This is the day, this is the day
   when the Spirit came, when the Spirit came;
   we will rejoice, we will rejoice,
   and be glad in it, and be glad in it.
   This is the day when the Spirit came;
   we will rejoice and be glad in it.
   This is the day, this is the day
   when the Spirit came.

44 We are marching in the light of God

Words: traditional South African trans. Anders Nyberg
Music: traditional South African arr. Noel Rawsthorne

* *Optional 2nd part.*
To create further verses, 'marching' may be replaced with 'dancing', 'singing', 'praying', etc.

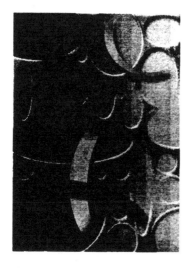

45 We have a King who rides a donkey

Words: Fred Kaan
Music: traditional arr. Noel Rawsthorne

2. Trees are waving a royal welcome,
   trees are waving a royal welcome,
   trees are waving a royal welcome
   for the King called Jesus.

3. We have a King who cares for people,
   we have a King who cares for people,
   we have a King who cares for people
   and his name is Jesus.

4. A loaf and a cup upon the table,
   a loaf and a cup upon the table,
   a loaf and a cup upon the table
   bread-and-wine is Jesus.

5. We have a King with a bowl and towel,
   we have a King with a bowl and towel,
   we have a King with a bowl and towel
   Servant-King is Jesus.

6. What shall we do with our life this morning?
   What shall we do with our life this morning?
   What shall we do with our life this morning?
   Give it up in service!

Verse 4 is suitable for Communion

46 When God made the garden of creation

Words and Music: Paul Booth
arr. Norman Warren

2. When God made the hamper of creation,
   he filled it full of his love;
   when God made the hamper of creation,
   he saw that it was good.
   There's food for you, and food for me,
   and food for ev'ryone:
   but often we're greedy, and waste God's bounty,
   so some don't get any at all.
   When God made the hamper of creation,
   he filled it full of his love.

3. When God made the fam'ly of creation,
   he made it out of his love;
   when God made the fam'ly of creation,
   he saw that it was good.
   There's love for you, and love for me,
   and love for ev'ryone:
   but sometimes we're selfish, ignore our neighbours,
   and seek our own place in the sun.
   When God made the fam'ly of creation,
   he made it out of his love.

4. When God made the garden of creation,
   he filled it full of his love;
   when God made the garden of creation,
   he saw that it was good.
   There's room for you, and room for me,
   and room for ev'ryone:
   for God is a Father who loves his children,
   and gives them a place in the sun.
   When God made the garden of creation,
   he filled it full of his love.

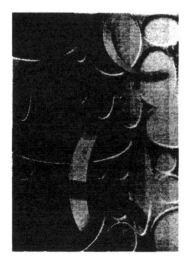

47   When I needed a neighbour

Words and Music: Sydney Carter
arr. Noel Rawsthorne

2. I was hungry and thirsty,
   were you there, were you there?
   I was hungry and thirsty,
   were you there?

3. I was cold, I was naked,
   were you there, were you there?
   I was cold, I was naked,
   were you there?

4. When I needed a shelter
   were you there, were you there?
   When I needed a shelter
   were you there?

5. When I needed a healer
   were you there, were you there?
   When I needed a healer
   were you there?

6. Wherever you travel
   I'll be there, I'll be there,
   wherever you travel
   I'll be there.

Final Refrain:
And the creed and the colour
and the name won't matter,
I'll be there.

48 When your Father made the world *Care for your world*

Words: Anne Conlon
Music: Peter Rose arr. Norman Warren

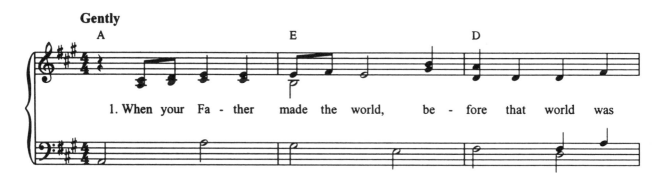

1. When your Fa - ther made the world, be - fore that world was

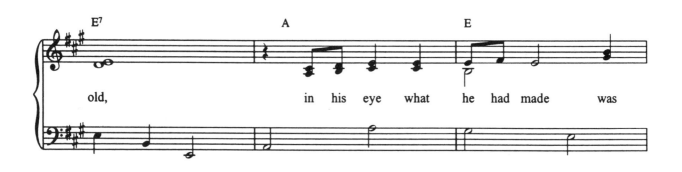

old, in his eye what he had made was

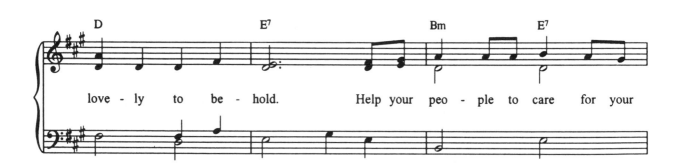

love - ly to be - hold. Help your peo - ple to care for your

world. The world is a gar - den you made, and

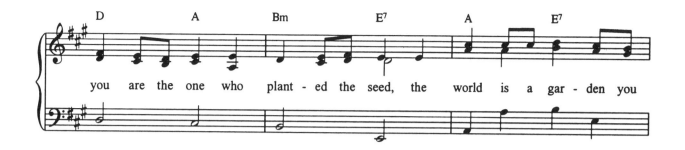

you are the one who plant - ed the seed, the world is a gar - den you

made, a life for our food, life for our joy,

life we could kill with our self - ish greed.

2. All the world that he had made,
   the seas, the rocks, the air,
   all the creatures and the plants he gave into our care.
   Help your people to care for your world.

3. When you walked in Galilee,
   you said your Father knows
   when each tiny sparrow dies, each fragile lily grows.
   Help your people to care for your world.

4. And the children of the earth,
   like sheep within your fold,
   should have food enough to eat, and shelter from the cold.
   Help your people to care for your world.

49 Who put the colours in the rainbow?

Words and Music: Paul Booth
arr. Noel Rawsthorne

1. Who put the colours in the rainbow? Who put the salt into the sea?
Who put the hump upon the camel? Who put the neck on the giraffe?
Who put the cold into the snowflake? Who made you and me?
Who put the tail upon the monkey? Who made hyenas laugh?
Who made whales and snails and quails? Who made hogs and dogs and frogs?
Who made bats and rats and cats? Who made ev'rything?

2. Who put the gold into the sunshine?
Who put the sparkle in the stars?
Who put the silver in the moonlight?
Who made Earth and Mars?
Who put the scent into the roses?
Who taught the honey bee to dance?
Who put the tree inside the acorn?
It surely can't be chance!
Who made seas and leaves and trees?
Who made snow and winds that blow?
Who made streams and rivers flow?
God made all of these!

50 You shall go out with joy

The trees of the field

Words and Music: Stuart Dauermann
arr. Christopher Tambling